Published in Great Britain in 2016 by Canongate Books Ltd,
14 High Street, Edinburgh EH1 1TE

www.canongate.tv

1

British Library Cataloguing-in-Publication Data
A catalogue record for this book is available on
request from the British Library

ISBN 978 1 78211 375 1

PEANUTS written and drawn by Charles M. Schulz
Edited by Jenny Lord and Andy Miller
Design: Rafaela Romaya
Layout: Stuart Polson

Printed in China by C&C Offset Printing Co, Ltd

CHARLES M. SCHULZ

THE PEANUTS GUIDE TO
FRIENDSHIP

CANONGATE

Edinburgh · London

FRIENDSHIP IS SMOOTHING A RUFFLED FEATHER

YOU CAN
CHOOSE YOUR
FRIENDS BUT
YOU CAN'T
CHOOSE YOUR
RELATIVES

DEAR MOM AND DAD,
THINGS ARE GOING BETTER HERE AT CAMP.
Yesterday I met this kid named Charlie Brown.

SOME FRIENDSHIPS ARE DOOMED FROM THE VERY BEGINNING!

SOMETIMES PEOPLE WHO LIKE YOU HATE YOU!

HAPPINESS IS A THOUGHTFUL FRIEND

MAN'S BEST FRIEND IS HIS BLANKET

DOGS ACCEPT
PEOPLE
FOR WHAT
THEY ARE

A LITTLE
FRIENDLY
CRITICISM
CAN BE
HELPFUL
TO A PERSON

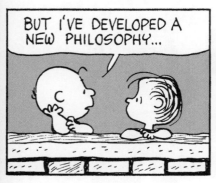